Nenookaasi Mawadishiwe
Hummingbird Visits

ogii-ozhibii'aan gaye ogii-mazinibii'aan
written and illustrated by

Erin Leary

Hidden Timber Books

Erin Leary/Hidden Timber Books
6650 West State Street, #D98
Milwaukee, WI/53213
www.hiddentimberbooks.com

Book design by Erin Leary
Illustrations by Erin Leary | Translations by Margaret Noodin

Ordering Information: Special discounts are available on quantity purchases by corporations, associations, and others. For details, contact the publisher at the address above.

Nenookaasi Mawadishiwe: Hummingbird Visits
ISBN 978-1-7365519-3-6
Printed in the United States of America

Electa Quinney Wiidookaagewigamig gii-ozhitoon o'o mazina'igan.

This book was created in partnership with the Electa Quinney Institute.

Niibin, waabigwaniin baashkaabigwaniig, gaye manidoonsag babaamisewaad ge ani-abaateg.

It is summer, flowers are blooming, insects are flying about, and the weather is warming up.

1

Wa'aw nenookaasiins abi owadiswaning.

This little hummingbird sits in his nest.

Gwiiwizensiwi wenji-makadewaandeg okaakiganing.
Apii onitaawigi wii-miskwaandeg okaakiganing.

He is a young male which is why he has a black color on his chest. When he grows up, his chest will be red.

Naabeseg eta godagigwanewag.

Only males have these marks on their feathers.

Aabiding, nenookaasi animaashi bijiinag dash
bakaded wenji-nandawenjiged.

One morning, the hummingbird flies from his nest for
the first time because he is hungry. He looks for food.

Manidoonsan odamwaan miinawaa banaskandang waabigwanaaboo.

He eats insects and slurps nectar from flowers.

Aanawi wa'aw nenookaasi gaawiin odebisatoosiin waabigwaning dash wenji-bwaa-minawaanigozid.

But there are not enough flowers so this hummingbird is not happy.

Dash nimbagidinamawaanaan ziinzibaakwadaaboo aabitaa-mooshkineg omoodayaabikong onagoodooyaang.

So we offer sugar water in a hanging bottle.

Wa'aw nenookaasi obagamise gaye obanaskandaan waabigwanaaboo ge aabajitood odenaniw.

This hummingbird arrives flying and buzzing and drinks nectar using his tongue.

Omaamawi-minwendaanan nenookaasi miskwaawaabigwaniin wen-ji-atemigag imaa omoodayaabikong.

The hummingbird likes the red flowers on the bottle.

Wa'aw nenookaasi oganawendaan o'o omoodayaabik dash gaawiin daa-minikwesigwaa bakaan nenookaasiwag.

This hummingbird protects his feeder so other hummingbirds will not drink here.

Apabiwaadaan wadiswaning dash ganawaabamaad bakaan nenookaasiwan.

He sits on the branch and watches the other hummingbirds.

Apii dash besho inaagoziwan, maajinizha'aad.

When they are close, he chases them off.

Dash obanaskandaan waabigwanaaboo gaye ogii-amawaan manidoonsan wenji-minawaanigozid.

Then he sips the nectar and eats insects, which makes him happy.

Ishkwaaji-niibinong apii odebisinii dash ani-biboonagag wenji-ozhiitaad wii-anda-biboonishid.

At the end of the summer when he has eaten enough, he prepares to migrate for the winter.

Animibizo zhaawanong gaye anoonji-giizhoozid
wenji-dazhiiked gabe-biboong.

He flies away to the south where it is warm,
and he stays there all through the winter months.

Noongom waabigwaniin ani-baashkaabigwaniiwan manidoonsag babaamisewaad, gaye ani-abaateg.

Now the flowers are beginning to bloom, insects are flying around, and the weather is warming.

Wayiiba wa'aw nenookaasi wii-azhegiiwe giiwedinong.

Soon this hummingbird will return.

Nindakawaabamaanaan gaye nindagoodoomin omoodayaabik.

We watch for him, and we hang the nectar.

Apii o'azhegiiwe wii-miskwaandeg okaakiganing.

When he returns, we will know him by the red marks on his chest.

23

Owii-dagoshimaan akawe naabesen nenookaasiwan dash noozhesen nenookaasiwan wii-biminizha'igoowaad.

He arrives first with the male hummingbirds,
and the female hummingbirds will follow them.

25

Onenookaasiinsiman wii-niigiwan...

His little hummingbirds will be born...

...mii dash wii-animaashinid dash bakadenid
wenji-nandawenjigenid.

...and then they will fly from their nest and be hungry.
They will look for food.

Giwii-bamenimaag ina?
Giwii-bagidinamawaa ina ziinzibaakwadaaboo
omoodayaabikong onagoodooyan?

Will you take care of them?
Will you offer sugar water in a hanging bottle?

Giishpin ashamadwaa, nenookaasiwag gidaa-mawadishigoog.

If you feed the hummingbirds, they will visit you again and again.

www.ojibwe.net

Ojibwemowin (or Anishinaabemowin as it is called by many speakers) is the first language of a vast landscape that includes most of Michigan and Ontario, northern Minnesota and Wisconsin and even parts of Alberta. Sadly, the language is endangered with speakers being lost more quickly than are being gained. The language is beautiful and ancient and conveys a unique way of seeing the world.

This book is an extension of greater work not only to help preserve the language but to use it. We invite anyone who is interested to learn and use these wonderful sounds and support the revitalization of indigenous language by visiting ojibwe.net for lessons, stories, songs, and more. The Ojibwe People's Dictionary at ojibwe.lib.umn.edu, a searchable, talking Ojibwe-English dictionary that features the voices of Ojibwe speakers, is another wonderful resource.

A Note about Dialects: This version uses what is commonly known as a western double vowel spelling system, but we honor and recognize all the dialects of Anishinaabemowin and hope this story will be shared widely.

Erin Leary
Author and Illustrator

Erin Illinois onjibaa. Illinois miinawaa Michigan daa noongom. Ogikinawaabi, onanda-gikendaan miinawaa omazinibiige. Onanda-gikendaan skiing gaye nanda-gikenimaad Anishinaaben. Ogii-nanda-gikendaanan dibaajimowinan Giiwedin-Ningaabii'an Gabe-gikendaas-owigamigong mii noongom nanda-gikendang Michigan Gabe-gikendaasowigamigong. Omaajii-anishinaabmo miinawaa o'o mazina'igan *Nenookaasi Mawadishiwe* wii-wiidookawaad ji-anishinaabemowaad. Owaabanda'aan ezhi-minwendang akiing mazina'iganing. Iniw nenookaasiwan Erin gii-mazinibii'aad mawidashiwenid endaad. Erin miinawaa odinawemaaganim nenookaasiwan waabamaad endaaso niibing apii dagoshinowaad.

Originally from Illinois, Erin lives now in Illinois and Michigan. She is a student, scholar, and artist whose work focuses on environmental and Indigenous Studies. She holds a BA in English literature from Northwestern University, and is currently a PhD student in the American Culture program at the University of Michigan. She is beginning to learn Anishinaabemowin (Ojibwe), and wrote this book *Hummingbird Visits* as a way to help herself and other language-learners practice. This book and all of Erin's work is a reflection of her love for the environment and our more-than-human kin. The hummingbird in this book is one who visits Erin's backyard. She and her family love watching this hummingbird and others grow and return each year.

Margaret Noodin
Translator

Maaganiit O'Donnell Noodin izhinikaazo Giiwedin Noodin Anishinaabemong miinawaa mewinzha o'aanikoobijiganibaniin Ojibwemonid mii wenji-Ojibwemod noongom. Ogii-naagad-awaabandaan ezhi-inaweyang, ezhi-dibaajimoyang gaye ezhi-ozhibii'igeyang Gichigabegikendaasowigamigong-Minnesota-Gakaabikaang. Noongom gikinoo'amaage Gichigabegikendaaso-wigamigong-Wisconsing-Minowakiing. Ogii-ozhibii'aan *Bawaajimo: A Dialect of Dreams in Anishinaabe Language and Literature* miinawaa niizh daso mazina'iganan Anishinaabemong gaye Zhaaganaashimong ezhinikaadeg *Weweni* gaye *Ezhi-Gikendaan Gijigijigaaneshiinh*. Ogii-aanikanootaabii'aanan nawaj apii nisimidana daso mazina'iganan Anishinaabemong ji-agindaminid abinoojiin. Oditan www.ojibwe.net ji-waabandaman miinawaa bizindaman gaa-giizhenindang.

Margaret O'Donnell Noodin received an MFA in Creative Writing and a PhD in English and Linguistics from the University of Minnesota. She is Professor of English and Associate Dean of the Humanities at the University of Wisconsin–Milwaukee. Noodin is author of *Bawaajimo: A Dialect of Dreams in Anishinaabe Language and Literature* and two collections of poetry in Anishinaabemowin and English, *Weweni* and *What the Chickadee Knows*. She has also translated over 30 books for children into Ojibwe. To hear her work, visit www.ojibwe.net.

CPSIA information can be obtained
at www.ICGtesting.com
Printed in the USA
LVHW071131130423
744090LV00002B/2